The Mathmaker
More Cooperative Learning in Math

by
Bob Bernstein

illustrated by Bron Smith

Cover by Bron Smith

Copyright © 1993, Good Apple

ISBN No. 0-86653-741-4

Printing No. 987654321

Good Apple
1204 Buchanan St., Box 299
Carthage, IL 62321-0299

A Paramount Communications Company

Dedication

Creating and writing the pages for this book have been challenging and rewarding. The challenge is in continually trying to create ideas that motivate and stimulate the thinking process as well as build a strong positive self-esteem. The reward is knowing that youngsters across the nation are involved in these activities that encourage thinking, reasoning and the enjoyment of learning.

Once I completed writing these pages, I thought about this page . . . the dedication page.

Immediately I began to think about my best friends, my greatest admirers . . . Leonora, Alan and Robyn Bernstein, my wife and my children.

Then I thought about friends who have passed away . . . my mom and dad and my father-in-law . . . Max and Estelle Bernstein and Paul Paolillo.

My thoughts then went to friends who helped me when I was first appointed to an elementary classroom . . . friends like the principal, Joe Robinson, and a director like Lore Rasmussen who said things such as "This young man will go far . . . . His creativity is outstanding." I can still see that smile that Joe gave to an almost brand-new teacher.

In a dedication you recall friends who constantly encourage you . . . friends such as Lowell and Brenda Fishman, Max and Marlene Wald, Larry and Verna Snyder, Fred and Rita Donatucci, Micki Ruskin and Audrey Badger.

And then there are the students who "made my day!" Students like Ian Baylis, Traffinia Starling and Qiana Miller.

And then there is a stranger who has faith in what you do, and he encourages you to write. He is also an author and a friend of mine, Jerry Aten.

To all of these people, I dedicate this book and I say . . .

Thank you,
Bob

Table of Contents

GA1456

Introduction

"You know, Mr. Bernstein, Qiana is really good at working with fractions. She showed us (group members) a really cool way to add the fractions that have unlike denominators. I didn't think that math was her subject. She's good!"

How about the time Cory grinned from one ear to the other when he brought victory to his group, because of his uncanny ability to estimate? As I moved from group to group, I couldn't help but notice this fifth grader with a huge smile. I mean a really big smile. The kind of gigantic smile that you just can't miss. This child had done something great, and he was being admired for it. He was getting a strong sense of positive self-esteem; and best of all, this was coming from his peers. This was a particular child who needed this kind of attention and he got it and he really earned it.

These are examples of cooperative learning–the working together in groups, the learning, the reasoning, the thinking and the sharing.

These experiences are important in learning about math, but these experiences are also most important in everyday life situations. It is a decent way to treat a fellow student as well as other people–with courtesy and respect.

But you know, if you stop and think about it, these are the exact things that great teachers have always done, and they have been doing them for quite a long time. It's just nice that these skills are being recognized.

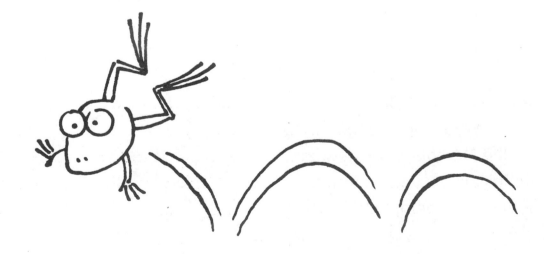

GA1456

The Dream Team

SKILLS: Averaging
Computation
Understanding decimals

Both Lois and Joey are excellent swimmers. Not only are they great at swimming, but they are exceptional divers off the high board. They are so good, both made the Delaware State Diving Championships.

In Lois' first dive, a forward spin with one and one-half turns, the ten scoring officials awarded Lois the following scores:

9.1 8.9 8.8 9.3 9.1 7.9 8.3 8.7 9.0 8.5

The highest score that any official may award is 10.0 .

To compute Lois' score for her first dive, the officials eliminated the highest score 9.3 and the lowest score 7.9 . The remaining scores were added and then the sum was divided by 8.

9.1
8.9
8.8
9.1
8.3
8.7
9.0
8.5
—
70.4

$$8 \overline{)70.4} = 8.8$$
$$64$$
$$64$$
$$64$$

Lois' score for her first dive was a very respectable 8.8 .

Joey's first dive was a backward one and one-half flip off the high board. It was an awesome dive. The officials responded with

9.0 8.9 8.9 9.4 9.5 9.1 8.8 8.9 9.0 8.7

Compute Joey's score and remember to toss out the highest and lowest scores first. Find the sum of the remaining scores and divide by 8. What was Joey's score for this exciting first dive?

1

The Dream Team

The following are the results of the three final dives for Lois and Joey. Your group is to arrive at the overall score for each diver.

Lois

2. | 7.3 | 8.2 | 8.1 | 6.8 | 7.0 | 7.6 | 8.4 | 8.2 | 7.9 | 8.1 | =

3. | 8.5 | 7.8 | 7.9 | 8.7 | 9.0 | 7.9 | 8.4 | 8.3 | 8.9 | 8.6 | =

4. | 9.2 | 9.3 | 9.3 | 9.5 | 9.4 | 9.7 | 10.0 | 9.3 | 9.5 | 8.6 | =

These are the official scores for Joey's final three dives:

Joey

2. | 8.4 | 7.9 | 8.4 | 8.1 | 8.8 | 8.3 | 8.9 | 8.2 | 9.0 | 8.9 | =

3. | 8.2 | 8.1 | 6.7 | 8.0 | 7.4 | 8.1 | 8.3 | 7.4 | 7.8 | 8.2 | =

4. | 8.6 | 9.2 | 8.4 | 9.5 | 8.3 | 9.5 | 8.1 | 9.6 | 9.5 | 9.0 | =

Questions:
  Who was the better overall diver, Lois or Joey?
  How did you and your group arrive at a decision?

The Dream Team

GA1456

Names _____

The Dream Team

There are many ways that your group as well as all of the other groups in the class can become The Dream Team.

Each group can use such things as
    math scores
    spelling scores
    social studies scores
    science scores

And in the school yard:
    Record sprint scores with a stopwatch. The five or six students in your group have their times recorded. Remember, toss out the highest score and the lowest score, and then find the sum of those remaining scores and divide.

You might want to compare your scores with those of another class.

The
DReam
team
"World's Highest
High Dive"

GA1456

Scavenger Hunt

SKILLS: Gathering and interpreting data
 Computation

The object for each group is to record names of common classroom objects on the Initial Letter Chart. Each group will be given five minutes to record words that begin with specific initial letters. Groups are to write their choices in the appropriate columns based on specific initial letters.

Once the five-minute period has expired, use the number that is located below each initial letter to determine the score for your group. To find out how many points you have, multiply the number in the column head by the number of words written in the column. When you total all five columns, you will have the score earned by your group.

Example:

Initial Letter Chart				
B **2**	**C** **3**	**D** **4**	**R** **5**	**T** **8**
books	chalk	door	room	telephone
boys	crayons	desk		teacher
board	chair			
basket	closet			
blocks	clock			
	class			
	children			

Scoring
5 *B* words x 2 = 10
7 *C* words x 3 = 21
2 *D* words x 4 = 8
1 *R* word x 5 = 5
2 *T* words x 8 = 16
    60 points

WELL,
IT'S NOT
IN THE
BEEHIVE!

GA1456

Names _____

Scavenger Hunt

Initial Letter Chart for Football				
C 40	F 45	G 51	R 63	T 75

Record as many football-related words as possible within five minutes; then multiply the number of words in each column by the number at the top of each column.

Total the five columns.

Compare your score with those of other groups.

Our score [ ]

Initial Letter Chart for Vacation Time				
C 65	F 100	H 105	M 115	S 120

Record as many words about vacation as possible within five minutes; then multiply the number of words in each column by the number at the top of each column.

Total the five columns.

Compare your score with those of other groups.

Our score [ ]

GA1456

Scavenger Hunt

Initial Letter Chart for Foods				
F 12	J 14	L 16	P 18	S 19

Our score [ ]

Record as many food-related words as possible within five minutes; then multiply the number of words in each column by the number at the top of each column.

Total the five columns.

Compare your score with those of other groups.

Initial Letter Chart for Weather Words				
C 20	F 26	H 31	P 42	S 45

Our score [ ]

Record as many weather words as possible within five minutes; then multiply the number of words in each column by the number at the top of each column.

Total the five columns.

Compare your score with those of other groups.

GA1456

Make 30, If You Can!

SKILLS: Problem solving
   Understanding equations

The task at hand, for your group, is to reach a sum of 30 by using only four addends. Each problem may only count toward your score if the initial letter of the problem is the next consecutive letter in the alphabet.

Problem 1

A	B	C	D	E	F	G	H	I	J	K	L	M	N	O
8	10	3	4	9	1	5	16	7	11	10	12	9	4	2

Example:
1. A   C   E   K

   8 + 3 + 9 + 10 = 30

According to the rules, the next problem must begin with letter *B*.

2. B   E   F   K

   10 + 9 + 1 + 10 = 30

The next problem must begin with letter *C*. And here is one additional rule . . . you may not use any letter that would come before *C*.

3. Acceptable . . .

   C   H   I   N

   3 + 16 + 7 + 4 = 30

Not acceptable: A problem that begins with any letter coming before *C* (A or B)

Lily Pad Fitness Course

29

30

GA1456

Make 30, If You Can!

Problem 1, continued

4. Continue this procedure until your group reaches a point whereby you cannot find four addends that will equal 30.

5. Scoring for each group will be done as follows:

[2 points] are awarded for each correct answer as long as the final sum is 30 and the initial letter in the problem is the next consecutive letter in the alphabet.

[5 points] are to be awarded for each correct answer with a final sum of 30 and with the 4 letters spelling a word.

Example:

C   H   I   N
3 + 16 + 7 + 4 = 30

List some additional answers that your group might find by using the letters and numbers on the previous page.

Share your results with the other groups in your class.

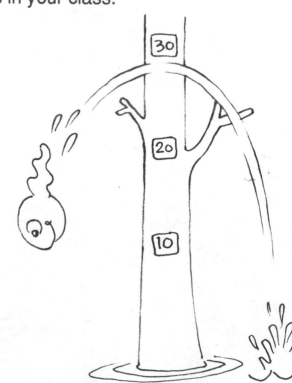

1. Letters:
   Numbers: _____ = 30

2. Letters:
   Numbers: _____ = 30

3. Letters:
   Numbers: _____ = 30

4. Letters:
   Numbers: _____ = 30

5. Letters:
   Numbers: _____ = 30

GA1456

Make 30, If You Can!

Problem 2

E	F	G	H	I	J	K	L	M	N	O	P	Q	R	S
9	1	3	10	4	13	2	5	6	15	12	6	8	1	10

1. Letters:
   Numbers: _____ = 30

2. Letters:
   Numbers: _____ = 30

3. Letters:
   Numbers: _____ = 30

4. Letters:
   Numbers: _____ = 30

5. Letters:
   Numbers: _____ = 30

6. Letters:
   Numbers: _____ = 30

7. Letters:
   Numbers: _____ = 30

2 points for each correct equation with a sum of 30

5 points for each correct equation with a sum of 30 and the order of the 4 letters spelling a word

GA1456

Make 30, If You Can!

Problem 3: Create your own letters and numbers. Pass this on to another group.

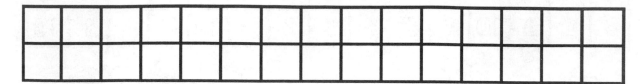

1. Letters:
   Numbers: _____ = 30

2. Letters:
   Numbers: _____ = 30

3. Letters:
   Numbers: _____ = 30

4. Letters:
   Numbers: _____ = 30

5. Letters:
   Numbers: _____ = 30

6. Letters:
   Numbers: _____ = 30

7. Letters:
   Numbers: _____ = 30

GA1456

Odd Triangle

SKILLS: Problem solving
       Patterning

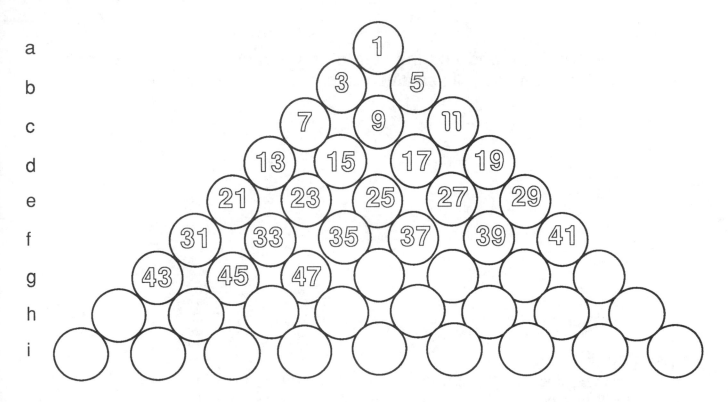

a
b
c
d
e
f
g
h
i

Complete this pattern of consecutive odd numbers. Once your group has done this, you will be given ten to fifteen minutes in which you will be asked to carefully examine the pattern, record your observations and prepare to report on your group's discoveries.

11

GA1456

Help with the Odd Triangle

When looking for patterns, refer to each row by the letter in front of it. This will help your group when it is time to record and report your findings.

Example:
Examine each row and find the sum of the numbers in that row. Look carefully because you will see a very interesting pattern evolve.

Row		Sum	
a	=	1	$\ldots = 1 \times 1 \times 1$
b	=	8	$\ldots = 2 \times 2 \times 2$
c	=	27	$\ldots = 3 \times 3 \times 3$
d	=	64	$\ldots = 4 \times 4 \times 4$
e	=	125	$\ldots =$
f	=	216	$\ldots =$
g	=		$\ldots =$
h	=		$\ldots =$
i	=		$\ldots =$

Another Finding:
$1 \times 1 \times 1$ is also . . . 1 to the third power or 1^3, one cubed
$2 \times 2 \times 2$ is also . . . 2 to the third power or 2^3, two cubed
$3 \times 3 \times 3$ is also . . . 3 to the third power or 3^3, three cubed

*There are some other interesting discoveries that are listed in the answer section of this book. Check to see if the findings of your group are the same as or different from those made by the author.

GA1456

High Rise

SKILLS: Problem solving
Patterning
Determining area
Multiplying

Each group will need up to 100 one-inch cubes or 100 one-centimeter cubes, whichever is more easily accessible.

Step 1
The problem calls for each group to choose anywhere from five to ten cubes. Someone in the group is to be designated the "builder" or "arch." With the chosen number of cubes, the "builder" is to construct a "building."

This sample building is constructed using six cubes.

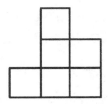

Step 2
After completing a sample building, each group will pass the sample building onto a neighboring group and accept their sample in return.

Step 3
The assignment for each group is to use the sample building as a reference.

Each group must create a new building that is TWICE AS LARGE AND IN THE SAME SHAPE as the sample building.

*Clue: l x h x w

13

GA1456

High Rise

Step 4

Upon completion of the new building, count the number of cubes required in its construction. The problem itself dictates that this number of cubes is a specific number and is related to the number of cubes used in the construction of the sample building.

Step 5

At this point, each group gathers data from all of the other groups once the required task has been accomplished.

Each group must record the number of cubes in the sample building and the number of cubes required to complete the building that is twice as large and in the same shape as the sample building.

*For additional practice, your team might want to go back to Step 1 and try another team's sample building and see if the new building contains the correct number of cubes.

Once all of the data is gathered, organize it into two columns:

Number of Cubes in the Sample Building	Number of Cubes in the Building Twice as Large and in the Sample Shape
Group A _____	_____
B _____	_____
C _____	_____
D _____	_____
E _____	_____

Look for some interesting results between the number of cubes used in the sample and the number of cubes used in the final product!

what happened to the high rise?

They built it with SUGAR CUBES!

High Rise Predictions

Your team should now be able to make predictions as to how many cubes are required to construct the final building once you have determined the number of cubes used in the sample building.

	Number of Cubes in the Sample Building	Number of Cubes in the Building Twice as Large and in the Sample Shape
1.	15 cubes	____ cubes
2.	18 cubes	____ cubes
3.	20 cubes	____ cubes
4.	23 cubes	____ cubes
5.	28 cubes	____ cubes
6.	40 cubes	____ cubes

Share your answers with other groups.

GA1456

More High Rise Predictions

More sample buildings.
More final buildings.

	Number of Cubes in the Sample Building	Number of Cubes in the Building Twice as Large and in the Sample Shape
7.	55 cubes	_____ cubes
8.	63 cubes	_____ cubes
9.	88 cubes	_____ cubes
10.	94 cubes	_____ cubes
11.	141 cubes	_____ cubes
12.	426 cubes	_____ cubes

HURRY! WE'LL BE LATE FOR WORK!

HIGH RISE

GA1456

X, X

SKILLS: Understanding place value
Understanding systems of numeration
Problem solving

The problem presented throughout this activity is for a special group or team of students.

Your group will receive very little information but will be expected to arrive at the correct answers. This is because all of you work well together and you exchange thoughts and ideas that help place all of the puzzle parts in order.

The following is a system of numeration. The placement of X is critical in the determination of a number.

Please observe the following clues very carefully.

| X $= 1$ | X $= 2$ | X X $= 3$ |

| X $= 4$ | X X $= 5$ | X X X $= 6$ |

X,X Rules Committee in Session

17

X, X

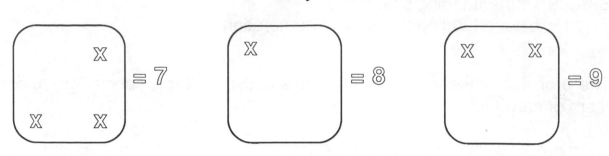

Refer to 8 and notice the placement of the X. Now refer to 9 and you will see one X in the eight position and another X in the one position. Therefore, $8 + 1 = 9$

The key positions in each box are

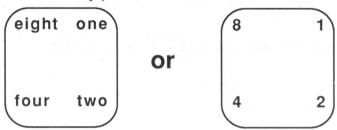

Before your group attempts to solve some of the following problems, it is most important you all recognize 10.

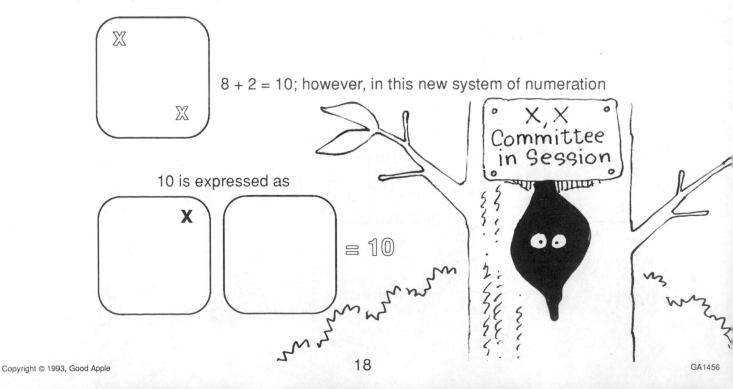

$8 + 2 = 10$; however, in this new system of numeration

10 is expressed as

$= 10$

X, X
Committee
in Session

GA1456

X, X

Some Additional Clues:

eighty	ten		8	1
forty	twenty		4	2

Again, concentrate on the placement of the X for the one's place and the **X** for the ten's place.

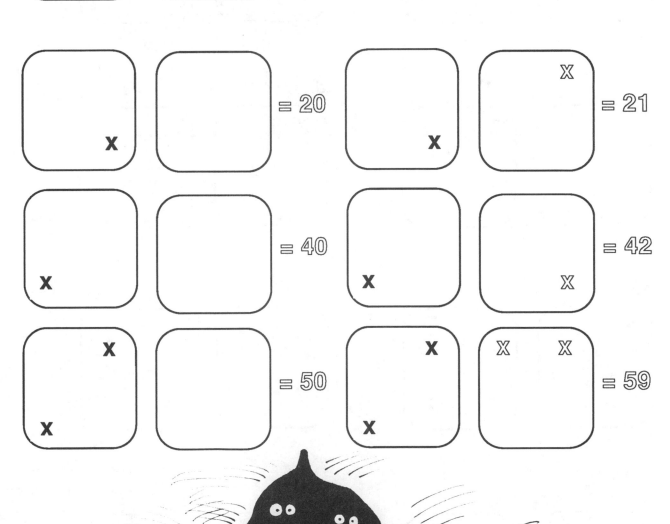

GA1456

X, X Practice

Names_____

Solve these.

a.

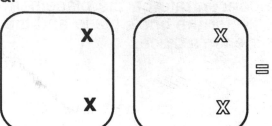

b.

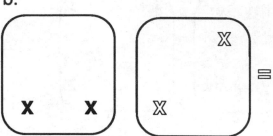

c.

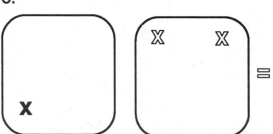

d.

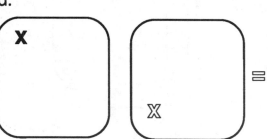

e.

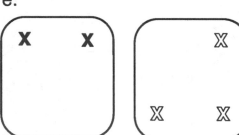

f.

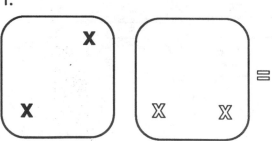

g.

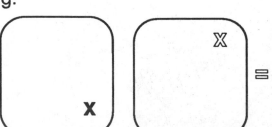

h.

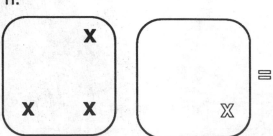

20

Names_____

More X, X Practice

Solve these.

i.
 = 15

j.
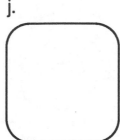 = 47

k.
 = 61

l.
 = 59

m.
 = 35

n.
 = 70

o.
 = 81

p.
 = 29

Names _____

X, X Challenge

q. Begin with 8; then square it and add 3.

r. Multiply 4 times 8; then add 19.

s. Divide 48 by 2; then subtract 18.

t. Find the product of 4 x 3 x 6.

u. Find the sum of 19, 18 and 34.

v. From 100, subtract 13 x 3.

22

GA1456

Prime Space

SKILL: Identifying prime and composite numbers

Most of the following are resort cities found in the state of New Jersey. Many of these cities share the coastline with the Atlantic Ocean.

The cities on this page are listed according to the number of letters that comprise the name of each municipality.

E l m e r	5
A v a l o n	6
C a p e M a y	7
W i l d w o o d	8
O c e a n C i t y	9
B r i g a n t i n e	10
S e a I s l e C i t y	11
A t l a n t i c C i t y	12
N o r t h W i l d w o o d	13
S e a s i d e H e i g h t s	14
L o n g B e a c h I s l a n d	15
W e s t A t l a n t i c C i t y	16
C a p e M a y C o u r t H o u s e	17

GA1456

Prime Space

Concentrate your group efforts on two New Jersey resort cities, Longport and Stone Harbor.

Look at the rectangular arrangements of the eight letters in *Longport*. Think of one letter in each of eight adjacent boxes.

Example:

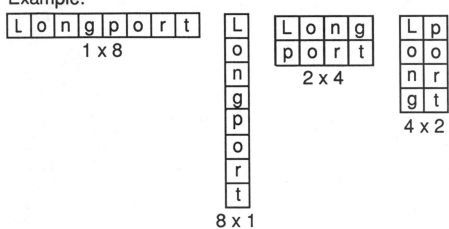

| L | o | n | g | p | o | r | t |
1 x 8

These are the possible rectangular arrangements for cities with eight letters.

Now look at a city with eleven letters, Stone Harbor:

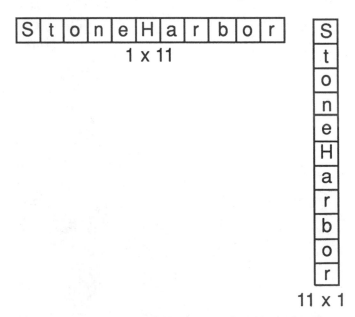

| S | t | o | n | e | H | a | r | b | o | r |
1 x 11

11 x 1

These are possible rectangular arrangements for cities with eleven letters.

Names _____

Prime Space

Refer to the page that lists New Jersey's cities beginning with *Elmer* and ending with *Cape May Court House*; then solve the problems on the following pages.

Your task is to make all of the possible rectangular arrangements that can be made using the letters in the name of each city.

When you have finished, record the cities that have exactly two rectangular arrangements. What numbers are associated with these cities?

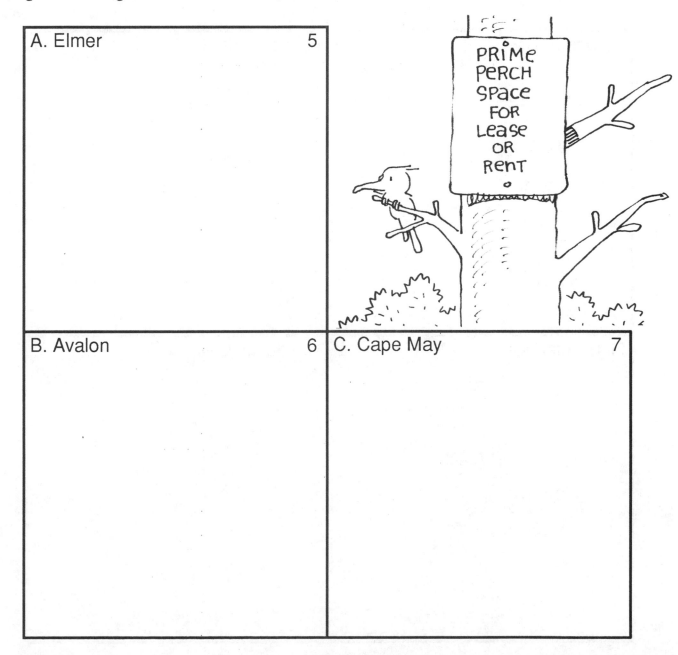

A. Elmer	5
B. Avalon	6
C. Cape May	7

GA1456

D. Wildwood   8

E. Ocean City   9

F. Brigantine   10

G. Sea Isle City   11

H. Atlantic City   12

I. North Wildwood	13

Names _____

north wildwood

seaside heights

J. Seaside Heights	14	K. Long Beach Island	15

L. West Atlantic City	16	M. Cape May Court House	17

Prime Space Challenge

Use an atlas to find cities anywhere in the United States that have the following number of letters:

18
19
20
21
22
23
24

You may have to use the combined number of letters in the city plus the state.

Once your team finds these cities, make all of the possible rectangular arrangements.

Question 1:
With what cities could your group make only two rectangular arrangements?

Question 2:
Would these same rectangular patterns emerge if your group used something other than New Jersey resort cities? Perhaps first and last names of family and friends?

GA1456

Round It Off

SKILLS: Estimating
Multiplying

With the ability to estimate, you have at your hands the awesome power to predict a sound and reliable answer to a problem. Your judgement will indicate to you what a correct answer looks like. You will immediately know whether or not your answer is sound and possible or ridiculous and way out of line.

If you are given the problem of multiplying 61 x 39, and without the power of estimation you arrive at an answer of 25,000, you may or may not be aware that the answer is incorrect.

With estimation, you would first round off 61 to the closest tens number—60—and round off 39 to the closest tens number—40. You would then be able to see that 60 x 40 = 2400. With an answer of 25,000 you might say, "Whoa! This answer is way off. I'd better go back and check my work because my answer is not even close."

The following activity will ask that you and your group members sharpen your skills at estimation!

You will be asked to round off factors to the closest tens number and then multiply.

The Letter-Facts Sheet on page 30 has ten problems for your group to solve. Each numbered row on the chart is a multiplication problem. The problem in Row 1 is $\mathbb{X}$ x $\mathbb{Y}$. Above the letter $\mathbb{X}$, you see the number 58. Above the letter $\mathbb{Y}$ is the number 47. Therefore, problem 1 is solved by multiplying 58 x 47. First record your estimation for each of the ten problems on the page. Then use a calculator to find the products, or exact answers. Compare your estimations to the products.

GA1456

Names_____

Round It Off: Letter-Facts Sheet

	29	58	47	63	79	18	31	81
	W	X	Y	Z	A	B	C	D
1.		✳	✳					
2.	✳					✳		
3.					✳		✳	
4.				✳			✳	
5.		✳						✳
6.	✳				✳			
7.		✳					✳	
8.				✳	✳			
9.				✳				✳
10.		✳			✳			

Round It Off

Estimation:
1. Use the Letter-Facts Sheet to create your own problems. Write them in the boxes.
2. Record the estimates.
3. Multiply to find the products.
4. Check your answers with calculators.

1. Example: Estimate ____ Product _____	6. Estimate ____ Product _____
2. Estimate ____ Product _____	7. Estimate ____ Product _____
3. Estimate ____ Product _____	8. Estimate ____ Product _____
4. Estimate ____ Product _____	9. Estimate ____ Product _____
5. Estimate ____ Product _____	10. Estimate ____ Product _____

GA1456

Alpha P.V.

SKILLS: Understanding place value
Understanding expanded notation

Alpha P.V. Chart

1000	100	10	1
a	h	o	v
b	i	p	w
c	j	q	x
d	k	r	y
e	l	s	z
f	m	t	
g	n	u	

Each letter in the alphabet has been assigned a place value column.

Example:

b = 1000

e = 1000

m = 100

n = 100

p = 10

t = 10

x = 1

z = 1

Use the Alpha P.V. Chart to determine the point value of *zebra*.

zebra		
z = 1		
e = 1000		3000
b = 1000	=	10
r = 10		1
a = 1000		3011 P.V.

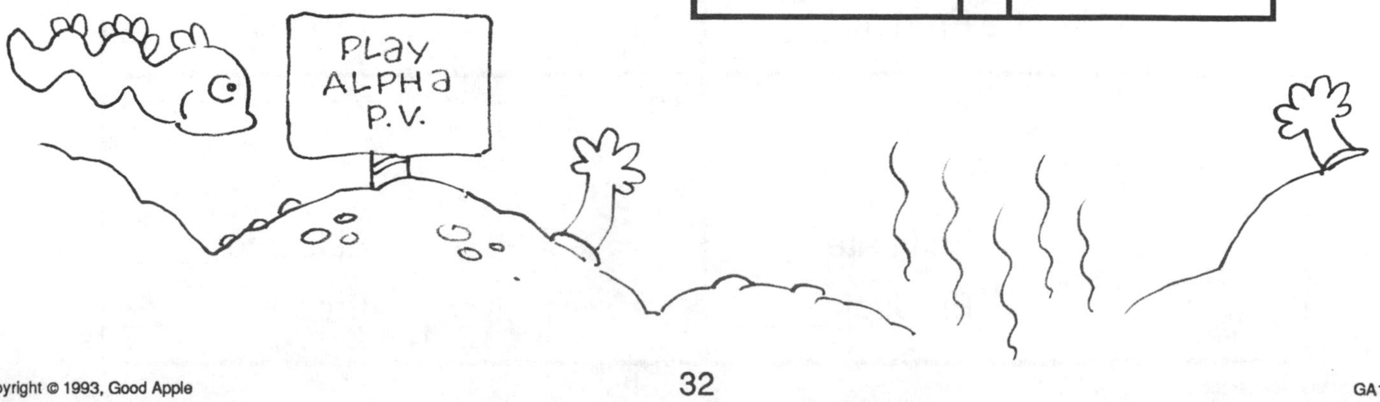

Alpha P.V.

Find the point value for each of the following words:

1.	class	
c =		
l =		
a =	=	
s =		
s =		☐ P.V.

4.	chalk	
c =		
h =		
a =	=	
l =		
k =		☐ P.V.

2.	lunch	
l =		
u =		
n =	=	
c =		
h =		☐ P.V.

5.	paper	
p =		
a =		
p =	=	
e =		
r =		☐ P.V.

3.	topic	
t =		
o =		
p =	=	
i =		
c =		☐ P.V.

6.	grade	
g =		
r =		
a =	=	
d =		
e =		☐ P.V.

GA1456

Alpha P.V.

On the previous page, all of the words were given to you and your group. You were asked to find the point value of each word by referring to the Alpha P.V. Chart.

On this page your group is asked to take a different approach. Your group will be given a point value and asked to find words with this point total. Again, your reference will be the Alpha P.V. Chart.

The task presented to your group is to find at least five words with a point value of 3100.

*Clue:
The point value of 3100 will indicate that the words you are looking for are made up of four letters. The 3100 point value also means that three of the letters come from the 1000 column and the fourth letter comes from the 100 column.

Our 3100 P.V. Selections

1. _____	6. _____
2. _____	7. _____
3. _____	8. _____
4. _____	9. _____
5. _____	10. _____

*Be ready with your proof.

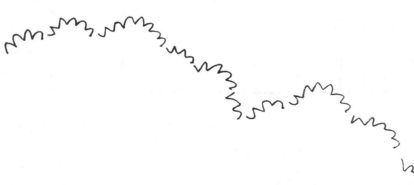

GA1456

Alpha P.V.

Who are these people?

Your group is to select the names of five classmates. Once these choices are made, your group is to find the point value of each name.

Once this is completed, announce the *point value* to the other groups. In other words, do not tell a classmate's name. Instead tell the point value of each of your five selections.

The task of your classmates is to determine the names of the five students chosen by your group.

We have chosen to give special recognition to

1. [   ] P.V. = _____

2. [   ] P.V. = _____

3. [   ] P.V. = _____

4. [   ] P.V. = _____

5. [   ] P.V. = _____

Who are these people?

DO NOT DISTURB— PLAYING ALPHA P.V.

Alpha P.V. Decimal Chart

Hundreds	Tens	Ones	Tenths
a	h	o	v
b	i	p	w
c	j	q	x
d	k	r	y
e	l	s	z
f	m	t	
g	n	u	

The procedure for determining various word point values is the same as those used with the original Alpha P.V. Chart.

The difference now is that you are working with decimals.

Use the Alpha P.V. Decimal Chart to determine the point value for:

zebra
z =   .1
e = 100.
b = 100.
r =   1.
a = 100.
301.1 P.V.

Hope he's not hungry.

Read the instructions above.

How do you use the Decimal Chart?

GA1456

Alpha P.V.

Find the point value for each of the following words:

1.   twist

t = .
w = .
i = .
s = .
t = .
_____ . P.V.

4.   exits

e = .
x = .
i = .
t = .
s = .
_____ . P.V.

2.   every

e = .
v = .
e = .
r = .
y = .
_____ . P.V.

5.   sweat

s = .
w = .
e = .
a = .
t = .
_____ . P.V.

3.   zesty

z = .
e = .
s = .
t = .
y = .
_____ . P.V.

6.   awake

a = .
w = .
a = .
k = .
e = .
_____ . P.V.

HeLP!
I don't have anyone to play ALPHa P.V. with.

Z

GA1456

Picture This!

SKILLS: Writing, drawing and creating story problems

In the rear of Alice's house was a large yard with 6 apple trees. All of the trees had apples, not too many, but there were some. Kyle counted 48 apples in all. The apples were large, red, delicious and juicy. Kyle told Alice that all of the trees had the same number of apples.

We would like to know exactly how many apples were on each tree. Can your group draw a picture so that we would be able to see the answer?

Please write the answer in a mathematical sentence.

Picture This!

Do you remember the problem about the 6 apple trees in Alice's yard? Well, it seems that three days later, Lisa found 50 apples on the trees.

Can your group draw a picture that would help everyone better understand the problem and how to reach a solution?

We would like to know how many apples were on each tree. As far as Lisa could determine, it appeared to her that each apple tree seemed to have almost but not quite the same number of apples.

Please ⎢draw⎥ the picture and ⎢write⎥ the answer in a mathematical sentence.

Picture This!

Names _____

Joann has a great hobby. She loves baseball, and she loves collecting baseball cards. When Joann is able to save enough money, she will buy 3 packs of baseball cards each week. There are 12 cards in each pack. How many new baseball cards will Joann have each week?

Draw the picture and write the mathematical sentence. Share your group's solution with the other groups in your class.

Additional questions regarding Joann and her baseball cards . . .

If Joann buys 3 packs of cards each week, how many cards will she have in 4 weeks?

Each pack of cards costs $2.00. How much money will Joann need for 4 weeks' worth of cards?

Picture This!

On July 1, Sara found a white and orange duck. You would probably call it a nice looking duck, that is if you were another duck.

Anyway, when Sara found the duck, it weighed 7 pounds. One week later, because of Sara's love and good care, the duck gained 5 pounds. It was exactly two weeks after this that the duck gained another 10 pounds. I know it may be somewhat difficult to believe, but exactly one week later this same orange and white duck gained one half its total weight. That is, the total weight after the third week.

And so the question is: what is the duck's weight now—at the end of the fourth week?

Can your group draw a picture of this problem? And please remember to also write your answer in a mathematical sentence.

Share your group's solution with the other groups.

Picture This!

Now it is your group's turn!

We want you to think about composing your own word problems.

Sit with your group and explore various ideas on just what kinds of word problems would be of interest to your fellow classmates. You know which topics will keep their interest.

Once the group has reached a decision on a **topic**, write the problem and work out the solution for yourselves.

You want to make certain that the problem is not too easy nor do you want it to be too difficult.

The problems should be interesting.

Cube It

SKILLS: Problem solving
Computation

Each face of the cube contains nine squares. The face of the cube measures 3 x 3. The cube has six faces. On the front face of the cubes below you can see that some of the squares are darkened (black) and that some squares are not darkened (white).

The front face of the cube replicates the other five faces. In other words, the black squares positioned on the front face are the same as the black squares positioned on the other faces.

Figure A   **Figure B**

1. There are [   ] black squares.   1. There are [   ] black squares.

2. There are [   ] white squares.   2. There are [   ] white squares.

43
GA1456

Cube It

Sample Cube 1

Consider the fact that all of the faces on the cube are numbered in the same sequence. Each square positioned on each face contains the same number.

If the same squares are blackened out on each face, what would be the point total for *each cube*?

Figure C

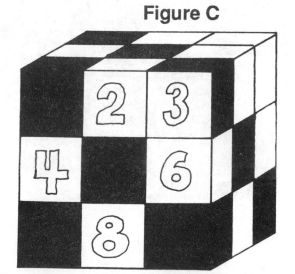

The point total of all the white squares is ☐ .

Figure D

The point total of all the white squares is ☐ .

How did your group arrive at the answer?

44

GA1456

Cube It

Refer to Sample Cube 1.

If the **same** squares are blackened out on each face, what would be the point total for *each cube*?

Figure E

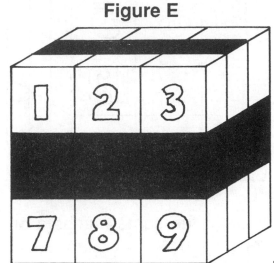

The point total of all the white squares is [____].

The point total of all the black squares is [____].

Figure F

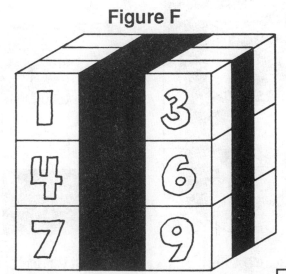

The point total of all the white squares is [____].

The point total of all the black squares is [____].

GA1456

Cube It

Sample Cube 2

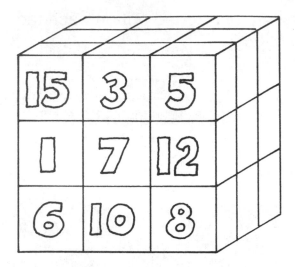

All faces on this cube have the same numbers on the same squares and in the same positions.

With the same squares blackened out on each face, what is the point value for the following?

Figure G   **Figure H**

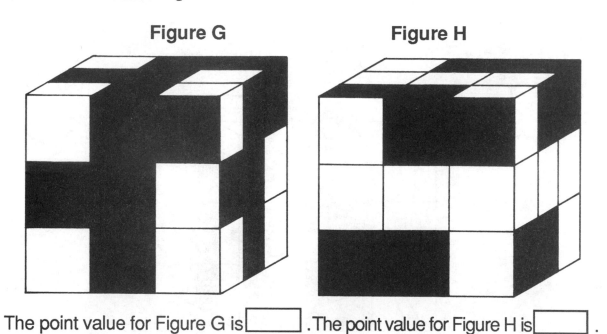

The point value for Figure G is [_____]. The point value for Figure H is [_____].

46

GA1456

And Still Another Way to Multiply

SKILL: Multiplication through problem solving

The power of 2 offers us an additional approach when it comes to understanding the process of multiplication.

Suppose we are given the following problem: multiply 31 by 17.

Consider the following:

16	8	4	2	1
A	B	C	D	E

Start with the E and write 31 below it. Now double the 31 and write the answer 62 below the D. Again, double this amount and write the 124 below the C. Repeat this process up to the letter A.

Each of the numbers written below each of the letters is a partial product of 31.

16	8	4	2	1
A	B	C	D	E
496	248	124	62	31

Another way of looking at these partial products:

Multiplication Chart for 31			
	Times		**Partial Products**
E =	1 x 31	=	31
D =	2 x 31	=	62
C =	4 x 31	=	124
B =	8 x 31	=	248
A =	16 x 31	=	496

47

GA1456

And Still Another Way to Multiply

We are to find the product for 31 x 17.
Refer to the Multiplication Chart for 31 shown on page 47.

Find partial products for

	Times	Partial Products
A =	16 x 31 =	496
E =	1 x 31 =	31
	17 x 31 =	527

Another example: 14 x 31

Find partial products for

	Times	Partial Products
B =	8 x 31 =	248
C =	4 x 31 =	124
D =	2 x 31 =	62
	14 x 31 =	434

Another example: 27 x 31

Find partial products for

	Times	Partial Products
A =	16 x 31 =	496
B =	8 x 31 =	248
D =	2 x 31 =	62
E =	1 x 31 =	31
	27 x 31 =	837

You might want to check these answers by doing the problems in the way you are accustomed to solving them.

```
  31        31        31
x 17      x 14      x 27
```

GA1456

And Still Another Way to Multiply

Complete the Multiplication Chart for 43.

List the partial products.

Multiplication Chart for 43			
	Times		**Partial Products**
E =	1 x 43	=	43
D =	2 x 43	=	86
C =	4 x 43	=	
B =	8 x 43	=	
A =	16 x 43	=	

After your group has filled in the partial products for 43, solve the following:

19 x 43 ⬚Times⬚ ⬚Partial Products⬚

_____

25 x 43 ⬚Times⬚ ⬚Partial Products⬚

_____

Don't forget to check your answers!

Names_____

And Still Another Way to Multiply

Complete the Multiplication Chart for 72.

List the partial products.

Multiplication Chart for 72			
	Times		**Partial Products**
E =	1 x 72	=	72
D =	2 x 72	=	
C =	4 x 72	=	
B =	8 x 72	=	
A =	16 x 72	=	

Solve the following and check your answers!

18 x 72   ⬚Times⬚   ⬚Partial Products⬚

_____

28 x 72   ⬚Times⬚   ⬚Partial Products⬚

_____

Suppose your group was asked to multiply 35 x 72.

GA1456

And Still Another Way to Multiply

Another challenge–this time another look at division.

When we multiplied and then added partial products, we used this pattern:

16	8	4	2	1
A	B	C	D	E

Just as you did when you were asked to multiply by 31, again start with E and write 31 below it. Next, double 31 and write 62 below D. Continue the doubling process until you have recorded the following:

16	8	4	2	1
A	B	C	D	E
496	248	124	62	31

The division problem asks you to take the number 558 and divide it by 31.

$$31\overline{)558}\quad\square\ \text{Control Box}$$

Refer to the A B C D E distribution. You are looking for the number closest to 558 without exceeding it.

Letter A offers 496. Subtract this number from 558 and, so as not to forget what you have done, record the 16 in the Control Box.

$$\begin{array}{r} \boxed{16}\ \text{Control Box} \\ 31\overline{)558} \\ \underline{496} \\ 62 \end{array}$$

And Still Another Way to Multiply

The remainder to the problem is 62. Since this number is greater than the divisor, 31, the problem continues.

Once again, refer to the A B C D E distribution. You are looking for the number closest to 62 without exceeding it.

Letter D offers 62. Subtract this number from the 62, and record what you have done in the Control Box.

```
                          ┌──┐
                          │16│ Control
                          │ 2│ Box
                          └──┘
              31 │558
                 496
                  62
                  62
```

The problem is completed. If you add the numbers in the control box you will discover that 558 divided by 31 gives an answer of 18.

Another problem:

┌────┐	┌────┐	┌────┐	┌────┐	┌────┐
16	8	4	2	1
A	B	C	D	E
496	248	124	62	31

```
                  ┌──┐ Control
                  │  │ Box
                  └──┘
      31 │438
```

Remember, you are to look for the number closest to 438 without exceeding it.

And don't forget to record in the Control Box.

Names _____

And Still Another Way to Multiply

1.

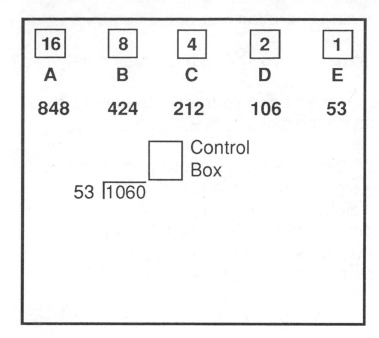

16	8	4	2	1
A	B	C	D	E
848	424	212	106	53

Control Box

53 ⟌1060

2.

16	8	4	2	1
A	B	C	D	E
416	208	104	52	26

Control Box

26 ⟌495

1492

SKILLS: Patterning
Performing operations on whole numbers

What can you do with fourteen ninety-two?

The challenge is for you and your team to look at, think about, consider and concentrate on the digits 1, 4, 9, 2.

Record at least 12 different ways of using the digits 1, 4, 9, 2 such as
  1. order the digits from high to low: 9, 4, 2, 1
  2. order the digits from low to high: 1, 2, 4, 9
  3. find the difference from 9421-1249 (8172)
  4. sort the numerals: even 4, 2; odd 9, 1
  5. find the sum of the digits 1 + 4 + 9 + 2 = 16

And now, it is up to you and your group.

1. _____   7. _____

2. _____   8. _____

3. _____   9. _____

4. _____   10. _____

5. _____   11. _____

6. _____   12. _____

P.S. Don't forget your names. _____ _____

                              _____ _____

                              _____ _____

GA1456

5 Picks to 70

SKILLS: Computation with regrouping

Materials:
A set of cards (2" x 3") for each group. The set is comprised of twenty-five cards. The cards are numbered 1 through 25 with one number on each card.

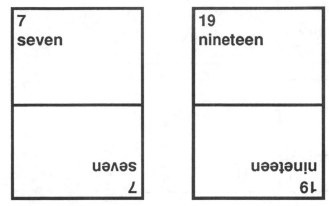

Each participating group will require a set of cards. The activity will last about ten minutes and follow this procedure:

The twenty-five cards are to be shuffled and then turned facedown. The cards should be arranged to form a 5 x 5 square. Players in the group will take turns exposing a total of up to five cards, one at a time.

After each card is uncovered, someone from the group is to record the number of the card on the score sheet. The objective is to reach a sum of 70 or to reach a sum as close to 70 as possible. Any sum greater than 70 is not allowed.

When the scores of all the group participating are compared, the group closest to 70 is the winner.

Once again it is not necessary to expose the limit of five cards.

GA1456

Names _____

5 Picks to 70

Example:

Team A 1.

18
eighteen

_____ 18 _____

2.

16
sixteen

16 + 18 = 34

3.

9
nine

9 + 34 = 43

4.

24
twenty-four

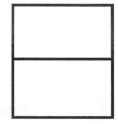

24 + 43 = 67

5.

_____

The members of Team A have a score of 67 and they do not wish to venture selecting a card that may put them over the 70 limit.   Our score   67

Each score sheet allows for two attempts to reach the 70 limit. The answers on the score sheet should be ranked in order. When each team is called upon to announce its score, the answer closest to 70 will stand for the team.

Names _____

5 Picks to 70

Score Sheet

1. ☐☐ _____

2. ☐☐ _____

3. ☐☐ _____

4. ☐☐ _____

5. ☐☐ _____

Our score ☐

1. ☐☐ _____

2. ☐☐ _____

3. ☐☐ _____

4. ☐☐ _____

5. ☐☐ _____

Our score ☐

Fabulous Fifty Cities

SKILLS: Mental math
        Computation
        Understanding exponents/binary system

The Fabulous Fifty Index gives you power. It allows you to know your classmates' choices as to their favorite cities. You will have the ability to know this without your classmates mentioning the names of the cities.

Ask one of your classmates to select any of the Fabulous Fifty Cities found on the index page. The person making the selection is not to disclose the choice to you.

After the selection is made, your classmate must carefully examine the page that contains the fifty cities listed in alphabetical order. The cities are also listed in columns headed by the letters A, B, C, D, E and F.

Once the selection is made, your classmate must disclose to you the column or columns in which the choice may be found.

Example:
Suppose the favorite city choice is Pittsburgh. Your classmate must not tell you the choice but instead must inform you as to the column or columns in which the choice appears. "My favorite city can be found in columns A, D and F."

For you to be able to identify the selection, you must give a numerical value to each column heading as indicated.

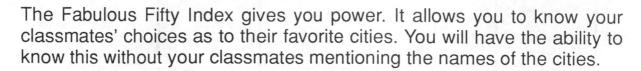

32	16	8	4	2	1
A	B	C	D	E	F

In the example above, the columns noted were A, D and F. If you use the values assigned to these columns, you will see

$$\begin{array}{ccc} A & D & F \\ 32 + 4 + & 1 & = 37 \end{array}$$

Refer to the Fabulous Fifty Index, and you will see that 37 is assigned to Pittsburgh. My, my, what power you possess!

GA1456

Fabulous Fifty Index

1. Acapulco
2. Atlanta
3. Baltimore
4. Billings
5. Boston
6. Butte
7. Charleston
8. Chicago
9. Cleveland
10. Columbus
11. Concord
12. Dallas
13. Denver
14. Detroit
15. Dover
16. Grand Rapids
17. Houston
18. Indianapolis
19. Jackson
20. Kansas City
21. Knoxville
22. Las Vegas
23. Lincoln
24. Los Angeles
25. Memphis

26. Mexico City
27. Miami
28. Montreal
29. Nashville
30. New Orleans
31. New York
32. Oakland
33. Oklahoma City
34. Omaha
35. Philadelphia
36. Phoenix
37. Pittsburgh
38. Portland
39. Princeton
40. Quebec
41. Richmond
42. Salt Lake City
43. San Antonio
44. San Diego
45. Scottsdale
46. Seattle
47. St. Louis
48. St. Paul
49. Topeka
50. Washington

GA1456

Fabulous 50 Index

A
- Oakland
- Oklahoma City
- Omaha
- Philadelphia
- Phoenix
- Pittsburgh
- Portland
- Princeton
- Quebec
- Richmond
- Salt Lake City
- San Antonio
- San Diego
- Scottsdale
- Seattle
- St. Louis
- St. Paul
- Topeka
- Washington

B
- Grand Rapids
- Houston
- Indianapolis
- Jackson
- Kansas City
- Knoxville
- Las Vegas
- Lincoln
- Los Angeles
- Memphis
- Mexico City
- Miami
- Montreal
- Nashville
- New Orleans
- New York
- St. Paul
- Topeka
- Washington

C
- Chicago
- Cleveland
- Columbus
- Concord
- Dallas
- Denver
- Detroit
- Dover
- Los Angeles
- Memphis
- Mexico City
- Miami
- Montreal
- Nashville
- New Orleans
- New York
- Quebec
- Richmond
- Salt Lake City
- San Antonio
- San Diego
- Scottsdale
- Seattle
- St. Louis

D
- Billings
- Boston
- Butte
- Charleston
- Dallas
- Denver
- Detroit
- Dover
- Kansas City
- Knoxville
- Las Vegas
- Lincoln
- Montreal
- Nashville
- New Orleans
- New York
- Phoenix
- Pittsburgh
- Portland
- Princeton
- San Diego
- Scottsdale
- Seattle
- St. Louis

E
- Atlanta
- Baltimore
- Butte
- Charleston
- Columbus
- Concord
- Detroit
- Dover
- Indianapolis
- Jackson
- Las Vegas
- Lincoln
- Mexico City
- Miami
- New Orleans
- New York
- Omaha
- Philadelphia
- Portland
- Princeton
- Salt Lake City
- San Antonio
- Seattle
- St. Louis
- Washington

F
- Acapulco
- Baltimore
- Boston
- Charleston
- Cleveland
- Concord
- Denver
- Dover
- Houston
- Jackson
- Knoxville
- Lincoln
- Memphis
- Miami
- Nashville
- New York
- Oklahoma City
- Philadelphia
- Pittsburgh
- Princeton
- Richmond
- San Antonio
- Scottsdale
- St. Louis
- Topeka

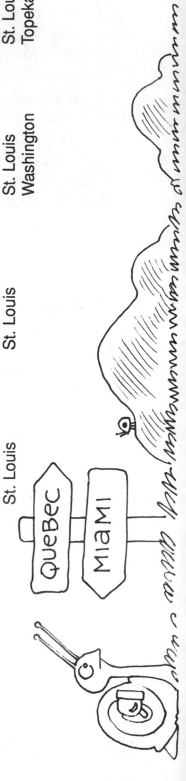

Quebec
Miami

GA1456

Fabulous Fifty Cities

Add the numbers marked with X in each row. The sum of these numbers and the Fabulous Fifty Index will give you the name of the city.

	A 32	B 16	C 8	D 4	E 2	E 1	=	Sum	Answer
Example:			X	X	X	X	=	15	Dover
A.	X			X	X		=		
B.		X			X		=		
C.	X		X	X			=		
D.		X		X	X	X	=		
E.			X	X		X	=		
F.		X	X	X	X		=		
G.	X				X	X	=		

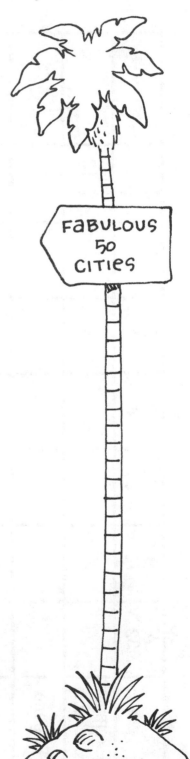

FABULOUS 50 CITIES

GA1456

Fabulous Fifty Cities

Use the Fabulous Fifty Index to complete the numerical distributions for the following cities.

	A 32	B 16	C 8	D 4	E 2	F 1	=	Sum	Answer
Example: Jackson		X			X	X	=	19	
Phoenix							=		
Nashville							=		
Topeka							=		
Memphis							=		
Las Vegas							=		
Cleveland							=		
Butte							=		
Montreal							=		

GA1456

Make It Happen!

SKILLS: Computation
       Working with equations

Each team is to write as many equations as possible in a ten-minute period. The equations must contain all of the numbers found inside the one large number. You may use the inside numbers only one time in each equation.

Example:

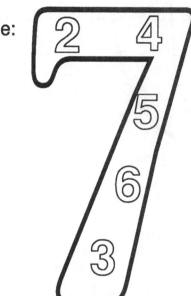

$$\left[(5-4) \times (3-2)\right] + 6 = 7$$

$$\left[3 - \left(\frac{6}{4+2}\right)\right] + 5 = 7$$

$$\left[(5 \times 3) - (6 + 4)\right] + 2 = 7$$

$$\left[\frac{(6+5) - 2}{3}\right] + 4 = 7$$

In each example, the end result is 7 and all of the inside numbers were used one time.

The following pages are similar to this example. Your group will have ten minutes for each problem. How many equations can you create?

where are we goin'?

We're gonna make it happen!

GA1456

Names_____

Make It Happen!

a. _____

b. _____

c. _____

d. _____

e. _____

64

Names_____

Make It Happen!

a. _____

b. _____

c. _____

d. _____

e. _____

Names_____

Make It Happen!

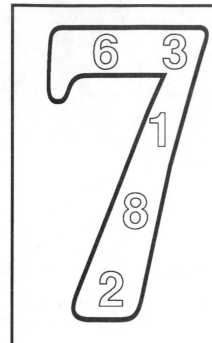

a. _____

b. _____

c. _____

d. _____

e. _____

66

Names_____

Make It Happen!

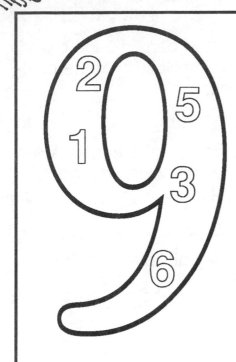

a. _____

b. _____

c. _____

d. _____

e. _____

GA1456

Common Sense

SKILLS: Problem solving
         Patterning

In each of the problems below you will find four members in each group. Each member is to be regarded as a clue to the disclosure of the common attribute shared by the four words in the box.

Consider the following examples:

A. | chair, dog, goat, table |

Common attribute _____

The four nouns in example A are not all made of wood. They do not all have tails.

The common attribute for these nouns is they all have four legs!

B. | eraser, door, desk, chalkboard |

Common attribute _____

The common attribute is they can all be found in school!

68

Common Sense

The task for your group is to work together and try to solve each problem by recording the common attribute shared by the four words in the box.

1. | smile, peach, crown, bacon |

Common attribute _____

2. | clock, thermometer, calendar, book |

Common attribute _____

3. | paper, pie, people, peanut |

Common attribute _____

4. | anaconda, comic, bulb, kickback |

Common attribute _____

5. | carousel, spin dryer, wheel, planet |

Common attribute _____

6. | nurse, doctor, intern, orderly |

Common attribute _____

GA1456

Common Sense

The problems on this page are more difficult.

Solve them at your own expense!

Go away! I'm playing Common Sense!

---

7. | never, seven, coves, level |

Common attribute _____

8. | shamrock, grass, leaves, frogs |

Common attribute _____

9. | boats, clam, seaweed, fish |

Common attribute _____

10. | John, James, Herbert, Millard |

Common attribute _____

11. | 1, 2, 3, 6 |

Common attribute _____

12. | 60, 105, 45, 90 |

Common attribute _____

GA1456

Common Sense

The problems on this page are the most difficult.

Solve them at your own expense!

Hey Mom! I can't do my Common Sense Work Sheet... my paper keeps getting wet!

13. bees, birds, planes, bats Common attribute _____	14. soda, tea, coffee, water Common attribute _____
15. stop, tops, post, pots Common attribute _____	16. Newark, Elizabeth, Camden, Trenton Common attribute _____
17. 7, 3, 11, 19 Common attribute _____	18. 6, 10, 15, 1, 5, 30 Common attribute _____

GA1456

Brainteaser XIII

SKILL: Problem solving

Where is it?

Where is the math word?

Somewhere in each of the following sentences there is a hidden math word. The math word still has all of its letters in the same sequence. The problem is that the letters that make up the word are separated.

Uncover them if you can. Each sentence has one math word.

Example:
1. Did you rub your arm on eye makeup?

   The math word is <u>m on ey</u>.

2. They called the plumber to drain Charlene's clogged sink.

   The math word is <u>in Ch</u>.

Try your skill at solving the thirty sentences on the following pages. Use the scoring range to determine how well you have done.

25 - 30 is super!

20 - 24 is great.

15 - 19 is good.

10 - 14 is not bad.

Brainteaser XIII

1. Charles sleeps late each and every day. _____

2. Will this get me a sure thing? _____

3. The best Tim ate was at lunch yesterday. _____

4. Really, I hope rationing won't be necessary this year. _____

5. Rebecca, please call in every once in a while. _____

6. Can your friend Ida talk about politics? _____

7. Can you please tell me who lent the book to Bob? _____

8. By doing this you may incur very harsh penalties. _____

9. After you warm up, how far can you throw the ball?_____

10. Please whisper, "I met Ernestine at lunch." _____

11. The clasp he reconstructed was incorrect._____

12. A powerful vitamin used in the program was small. _____

13. The car Ray was driving was blue._____

14. Has the railroad monopoly gone too far this time?_____

15. Ms. Brown wanted to drop Lane from the class list._____

GA1456

Brainteaser XIII

16. It seems that the falcon escalates in flight._____

17. The party is for Ty's homecoming. _____

18. We can reach orders much quicker in the fall. _____

19. Whenever we are a team, we win. _____

20. It is my good friend Conrad I usually admire. _____

21. Does Chip owe Ralph new baseball cards?_____

22. The food Diana provided was exceptional._____

23. We know that Steve never ate the tuna fish. _____

24. Who sang, "Leave Me at the Mall"? _____

25. Claude asked, "When do you cover a yak? _____

26. Did you find Leonora's umbrella after the rain? _____

27. Is it possible that Alpo™ interests many dogs? _____

28. The regal London atmosphere told us the queen was nearby._____

29. Please put the cup in the closet._____

30. Did you see the beautiful dress Pat wore last weekend?_____

GA1456

Brainteaser XIV

SKILL: Problem solving

License Plates Reference Box

1	2	4	8					
won	too	for	ate					
one	to							
B	C	I	O	P	R	T	U	Y
be	see		oh	pea	are	tea	you	why

Using the numbers and letters found in the Reference Box, see if your group can correctly decipher and then record the meaning of each license plate found on the following page.

Example:
Y R U L8?   = Why are you late?

W8 4 1 T BAG = Wait for one tea bag.

After your group completes the problems on the next page, try creating your own license plates.

GA1456

Names_____

Brainteaser XIV

Refer to the Reference Box on page 75 to decipher these license plates.

a. I C U 8 MY PS.

b. R U MY D8

c. 2DAY I C U 1.

d. Y, O Y, R U B4 US?

e. 50 ST8S

f. W8ING 4 U, 2

g. Y R U IN MY CT?

h. U 1. Y R U SAD?

_____

_____

_____

_____

_____

_____

_____

_____

GA1456

Names_____

Brainteaser XV

SKILL: Problem solving

Robyn and her family live in a high-rise apartment building overlooking a long and beautiful tree-lined river. Four of Robyn's best friends also live in the tall building.

Both Robyn and her friend Jill were on the elevator when it stopped at the tenth floor. Jill got off the elevator. This is the floor that she and her family live on. Ten floors is one-fifth the number of floors in the building.

Two floors from the top floor you will find Renee and her family.

If you start at the ground floor and go seven-tenths of the way up, you will see that this entire floor is a very fine restaurant. Three floors below the restaurant is the floor where Helene and her family live.

And by the way, Robyn's best friend Susan lives nine floors below Renee. Robyn lives on the first prime numbered floor after 20.

> Can you and your group answer the following questions?

1. How many floors are in the building? _____

2. On what floor does Renee live? _____

3. On what floor is the restaurant?_____

4. On what floor will you find Helene and her family?_____

5. On what floor will you find Susan and her family?_____

6. On what floor will you find Robyn?_____

Brainteaser XVI

SKILL: Problem solving

This problem will require critical thinking on the part of both you and your group. An excellent problem-solving skill would be the use of a diagram to help your team pictorialize a solution.

The Problem:
There are twelve beautiful homes in the beach block of South Madison Street. Each house is constructed with a large two-car garage. The problem is that all homeowners do not own two cars. Some houses have one car. Some houses have two cars, while some houses have three cars.

The task for your group is to arrive at the answer to this question: How many cars are in the beach block of South Madison Street?

I'm sure the following information will help.

a. Of the 12 homes on the block, $2/3$ of them have 3 cars.

b. $1/6$ of the homes have 2 cars.

c. The remaining homes have 1 car each.

Another Thought:
Every family on the block has children. How many children live on South Madison Street?

a. $1/4$ of the families have 2 kids.

b. $1/3$ of the families have 3 kids.

c. The remaining families each have 1 child.

GA1456

Brainteaser XVII

SKILL: Problem solving

The numerals recorded below are in the lettered form. Each letter is made up of straight line segments.

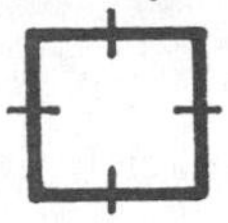

☐ = 4 line segments   E = 4 line segments

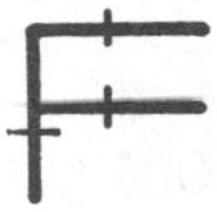

F = 3 line segments   X = 2 line segments

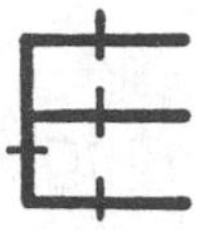

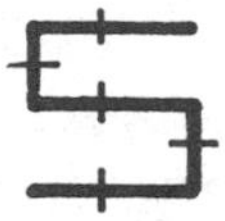

R = 5 line segments   S = 5 line segments

The word ONE

4 + 3 + 4 = 11 line segments

The word TWO

2 + 4 + 4 = 10 line segments

The word THREE

2 + 3 + 5 + 4 + 4 = 18 line segments

Come back later! We're working on BRAINTEASER XVII!

Brainteaser XVII

Use the sample letters on page 79 to help you and your group record the numerals in their lettered form and then total the number of line segments.

Four of the numerals from 1 to 24 contain 18 line segments. Can your group find them?

The first few numeral words are presented as an example to help guide your group.

FOUR ⁴	FIVE ⁵	SIX ⁶
FOUR _____ line segments	FIVE _____ line segments	SIX _____ line segments
7 _____ line segments	8 _____ line segments	9 _____ line segments
10 _____ line segments	11 _____ line segments	12 _____ line segments
13 _____ line segments	14 _____ line segments	15 _____ line segments

Brainteaser XVII

16 _____ line segments	17 _____ line segments	18 _____ line segments
19 _____ line segments	20 _____ line segments	21 _____ line segments
22 _____ line segments	23 _____ line segments	24 _____ line segments

*The numerals with 18 line segments are _____, _____ and _____.

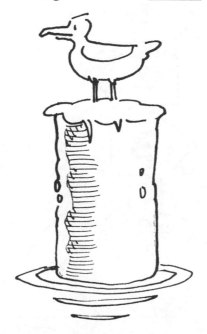

GA1456

Just How Important Are Numbers?

SKILL: Problem solving

If there were no numbers, I mean if all numbers were gone, lost, banished or even exiled, how would you know what floor you are on as you exit an elevator?

How would you know how tall you are?

How would you know what time it is when you wake up each morning or when to go to bed at night?

How would you know how fast an automobile is travelling so as not to get a speeding ticket?

How would you know how many days until Christmas, your birthday, or even how old you are?

How would you know your address?

How would you know what score you need to pass a test?

Just How Important Are Numbers?

Can your group write at least ten additional responses to the question, "Just how important are numbers"? Then share your group's responses with the other groups in your class.

If there were no numbers . . .

1.

2.

3.

4.

5.

6.

7.

8.

9.

10.

$1+1=2$ $3+3=6$
$5+5=10$ $2+2=4$
$7+7=14$
$10+10=20$
$9+9=18$

...math teachers would be underwater stump blasters or boneless chicken ranchers!

GA1456

The Pyramid

SKILLS: Computation
       Problem solving

To initiate this activity, each group will be assigned one of the five vowels: A, E, I, O, U. After a group is given its vowel assignment, the group will be asked to record its choice of any four consonants with the exceptions of X, Y and Z. These four consonants are to be placed in a sealed envelope, given to an opposing team and set aside until the ten-minute work period is completed.

The ten-minute work period is to be used in the following way:

Suppose the vowel E was assigned to group 1. The task for this group is to find and record as many words as possible that begin with the letter E. Another requirement is that each word must contain a specific number of letters.

Ideally, in ten minutes, each group will record eleven words. The first word will contain three letters, the next word will have four letters and so on to the last word. The last word will have thirteen letters.

Every word must begin with the designated vowel.

A helpful strategy is, rather than beginning with a three-letter word and working your way down consecutively to the thirteen-letter word, brainstorm and skip around to arrive at the necessary words.

Scoring is dependent on two things:
  1. The number of words that a team is able to record in a ten-minute period
  2. The selection of consonants given to your team by the rival team

Ten minutes?!
Who do you think
I am,
Albert Einswine?

The Pyramid

Perhaps after a ten-minute period, your team was able to record the following:

ego	= 3
even	= 4
early	= 5
estate	= 6
	= 7
everyone	= 8
enjoyment	= 9
	= 10
everlasting	= 11
	= 12
environmental	= 13

After the ten-minute period, opening the sealed envelope reveals the following consonants: F, L, M, N. This is how your group would compute its score.

The scoring value for F is zero because you did not use the letter F in any of your words.

L in early is	5	(five-letter word)
L in everlasting is	11	(eleven-letter word)
L in environmental is	13	
M in enjoyment is	9	
M in environmental is	13	
N in even is	4	
N in everyone is	8	
N's in enjoyment are	18 (9 x 2)	
N in everlasting is	11	
N's in environmental are	39 (13 x 3)	
	131 points	

The winning group will have the highest point total.

And the Pyramid winner is...

GA1456

The Pyramid

Each group will be given a ten-minute time period in which to record as many of the eleven words as possible. The initial letter for each word (A, E, I, O or U) will be given to you by your teacher. Your team will also receive a sealed envelope from an opposing group. This envelope will contain four secret letters. You will need these letters to score your words. Each mystery letter found in a particular word will have a point value equal in number to the number of letters in the word. Good luck!

Initial letter is ☐ .

☐☐☐ = 3

☐☐☐☐ = 4

☐☐☐☐☐ = 5

☐☐☐☐☐☐ = 6

☐☐☐☐☐☐☐ = 7

☐☐☐☐☐☐☐☐ = 8

☐☐☐☐☐☐☐☐☐ = 9

☐☐☐☐☐☐☐☐☐☐ = 10

☐☐☐☐☐☐☐☐☐☐☐ = 11

☐☐☐☐☐☐☐☐☐☐☐☐ = 12

☐☐☐☐☐☐☐☐☐☐☐☐☐ = 13

Our score ☐ Use this space
to compute your score.

GA1456

Beach Party

No, I'm not going...they're having a clam bake!

SKILLS: Problem solving
Patterning

It was a hot and sunny summer day when Robyn and her friends had a beach party. Robyn's mom was partly responsible for the beautiful display of cool and ripe fruit. The fruit was the party's refreshment.

The fruit became a party favorite because of the way it was displayed.

The fruit layout began with a grapefruit. This was followed with 2 pears and 3 plums. With each additional fruit laid out by Robyn's mom, the number of pieces of that particular fruit always increased by one—4 apples, 5 cherries, 6 bananas.

This pattern of increase continued through the following fruit:

peaches   blueberries
strawberries   oranges
melons   pineapples
grapes

Question 1:
How many pieces were on display?

Question 2:
Can you and your group record the process you used to arrive at your answer?

Question 3:
Suppose Robyn's mom displayed
   a. 20 different fruits. How many pieces of fruit would there be altogether?
   b. 25 different fruits. How many pieces of fruit would there be altogether?
   c. 40 different fruits. How many pieces of fruit would there be altogether?

GA1456

Say When!

SKILLS: Estimating
         Telling time
         Computation
         Understanding decimals
         Averaging

Each group will need a stopwatch, paper and a pencil. Player A will be in control of the stopwatch, which should be set at 0.00. When Player A says "Go," Player B is to estimate the passage of time—thirty seconds to be exact. When Player B thinks that thirty seconds has elapsed, Player B will say "Stop!" At this point, Player A will stop the watch and record Player B's score.

The objective is to see how well you can estimate the passage of thirty seconds.

Example:
Suppose Player B said "Stop!" and Player A, looking at the stopwatch, read twenty-two seconds. Then for round one, Player B would have a score of twenty-two.

Perhaps when Player B took a second turn and said, "Stop!" Player A looked at the stopwatch and the time read thirty-three seconds. The score for Player B for the second round would be zero. If a player says "Stop" and more than thirty seconds shows on the stopwatch, the player will not score points for that round.

Each player will take three turns at estimating the passage of thirty seconds. The score for each of the three rounds will be accumulated.

The winner will be the player with the combined three-round score that is closest to ninety.

GA1456

Say When!

If you have been working with decimals, then the scoring will change somewhat.

This time when a player says "Stop," it may not be exactly twenty-two seconds. If the stopwatch is so equipped, look for the score to reach into the hundredths of a second–22.87.

The winner will still be the player closest to 90 after three rounds.

*The best score to date is from a fifth grade student at Shawmont School in Philadelphia, Pennsylvania.
The student's score:
  Round 1: 28.97
  Round 2: 29.64
  Round 3: <u>29.08</u>
          87.69

You can find the average score for each round if you divide the sum by 3.

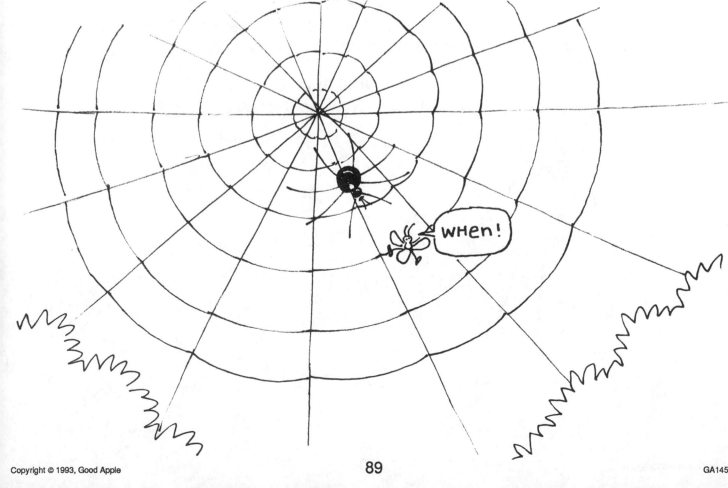

Names_____

Alabama to Wyoming

SKILLS: Gathering and interpreting data

The ability to gather data and interpret the data is powerful. This activity deals with your group's capacity and creativity in how you all decide to pass on to the other groups this gathered information that you will collect, based on questions concerning the fifty states all the way from the *A* in Alabama to the *W* in Wyoming.

As a unit, your group is to find the solutions to the following problems and graphically illustrate your findings.

Problem A:
1. Consider the initial letter in each of the fifty state names. What is the most popular initial letter?

2. Among the same fifty state names, what is the least popular initial letter?

3. Of all of the letters in the alphabet, there are seven letters that are not the initial letter of any state name. What are these letters?

With a good tail wind I should be in Wyoming in about 350 years!

Alabama to Wyoming

Problem B:

Utah has four letters.
North Carolina has thirteen letters.

Prepare a graph that will indicate to all groups the distribution of the number of letters in each of the fifty state names.

* There are four states that begin and end with the same letter. Which states are they?

Problem C:

Prepare a graph that will show the distribution as well as the total number of letters in all fifty state names combined.

1. What is the most commonly used letter in the fifty state names?
2. What is the one letter in the alphabet that is not used in any state name?
3. What is the total number of letters required to spell the fifty state names?
4. What is the average number of letters in the fifty state names?

Are we there yet, dad?

WYOMING OR BUST!

GA1456

Where's the Number?

SKILL: Divergent thinking

This activity is designed to see how well you and your group are able to diverge your thought processes. The boxes are numbered 1-8. Boxes 1 and 4 are examples. Each box carries with it the same theme–a unique method of representing a particular number. The task for your group is to decipher the numeral represented in each box.

The examples are to help you uncover the secret. Discuss the various possibilities brought up by your group members.

Example 1:

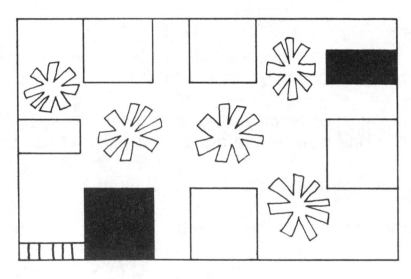

Example 2:

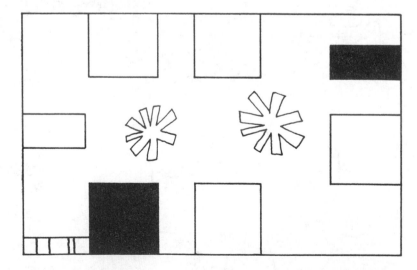

Example 1 is showing the number 6 .

Example 2 is showing the number 5 .

Names_____

Where's the Number?

Example 3:

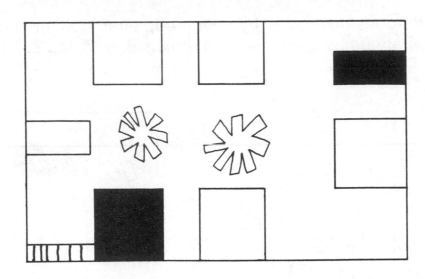

Example 4:

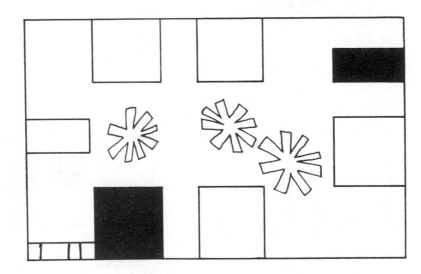

Example 3 is showing the number ⑦ .

Example 4 is showing the number ④ .

Carefully examine all four examples. Discuss your group's findings.

93

Where's the Number?

Using the theories developed by your group after looking at examples 1-4, decide what numbers are shown in boxes 5, 6, 7 and 8.

5.

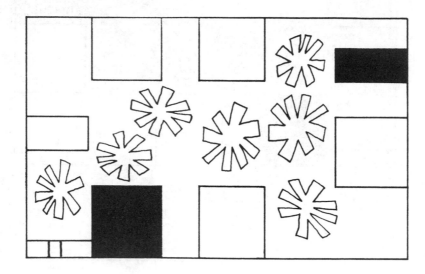

6.

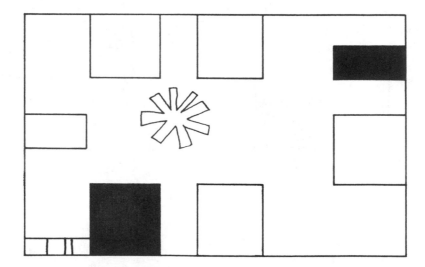

Box 5 is showing the number _____.

Box 6 is showing the number _____.

94

Where's the Number?

7.

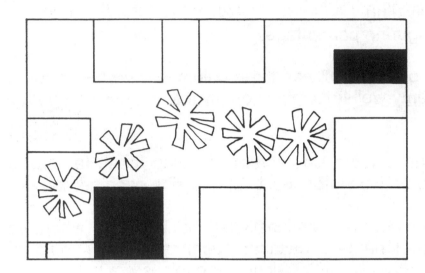

8.

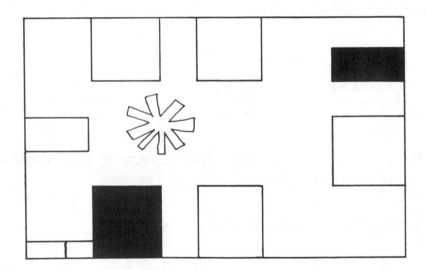

Box 7 is showing the number _____.

Box 8 is showing the number _____.

Our reasoning: _____

_____

95

GA1456

Famous Initials

SKILLS: Problem solving
Dividing
Figuring percentages

The chart on page 97 has three columns. The first column lists the initials of twenty well-known persons whose names can be found in history books.

The second column lists clues regarding these famous people. Each clue is one or two words that best describe each person.

The third column is intentionally left blank. This is where your group will record the full name of each famous person. You should work this problem out together by discussing your choices.

After a fifteen-minute period, your teacher will review the twenty sets of initials. Keep score by placing a check after each correct answer.

Example:

Initials	Clue	Response
J F K	Statesman	John Fitzgerald Kennedy

To determine the score for your group, count the number of correct responses and divide this number by 20.

Suppose your group had 16 correct responses.

$20\overline{)16}$

or

$$20\overline{)16.00} \quad .80$$
$$\underline{16.00}$$
$$0$$

The group score would be 80%.

*You and your group members might want to examine some history books to see if you can come up with your own list of initials of famous people.

GA1456

Famous Initials

	Initials	Clue	Response
1.	M L K	Civil Rights Leader	
2.	F D R	Statesman	
3.	D D E	Soldier-Statesman	
4.	L B J	Statesman	
5.	H S T	Statesman	
6.	R M N	Statesman	
7.	E A P	Writer	
8.	R L S	Writer	
9.	S B A	Feminist	
10.	T A E	Inventor	
11.	U S G	Soldier-Statesman	
12.	G W C	Scientist	
13.	R E L	Soldier	
14.	G B S	Writer	
15.	R W E	Poet	
16.	O W H	Statesman	
17.	J P S	Musician	
18.	H W L	Poet	
19.	J D R	Businessman	
20.	J W H	Feminist	

Famous Initials

	Initials	Clue	Response
1.	G S P	Soldier	
2.	B T W	Educator	
3.	W J B	Statesman	
4.	J F C	Writer	
5.	G A C	Soldier	
6.	M M B	Educator-Civil Rights Leader	
7.	G M C	Composer	
8.	W R H	Publisher	
9.	A G B	Inventor	
10.	J Q A	Statesman	

*These initials may be somewhat more difficult, but not for such a talented group as yours!

GA1456

My Poem, Your Poem, Our Poem!

SKILLS: Understanding word problems
Problem solving

The poem on the following page is for you and your group. It is up to your team to supply the necessary numbers for all of the empty boxes found in the poem.

Once the members of your team have decided on the numbers to be inserted in the boxes, you all must correctly solve the problem.

Do this before you pass the poem on to another group. Be sure your group has the correct answer.

In return, your group will get a problem from one of the other groups. The difference of course will be the numbers inserted in the blank boxes.

Solve their problem!

*Many classes have taken this idea to heart. You and your group may wish to create your own poem, and then it will become your poem, our poem!

GA1456

My Poem, Your Poem, Our Poem!

There were ☐ ducks swimming on a lake so blue,

while high overhead ☐ dozen geese flew.

They were all headed south in an orderly way,

passing ☐ swans who had little to say.

Near the water's edge, a flamingo stood tall,

as ☐ pelicans and ☐ dozen egrets were having a ball.

They all frolicked and romped while searching for dinner,

but a new bird appeared for it was the winner.

The prize was a fish that looked juicy and plump.

They could not believe it, those ☐ frogs on the stump.

All of the animals were looking for something to eat,

but it was the tiny seagull who became the animal to beat.

In this poem, there are ☐ animals mentioned. And this is our reasoning:

Answer Key

The Dream Team Pages 1-2

Lois
Dive 1. 8.8
2. 7.8
3. 8.4
4. 9.4
Overall 8.6
Joey
Dive 1. 9.0
2. 8.5
3. 7.9
4. 9.0
Overall 8.6

Make 30, If You Can! Pages 8-9
Page 8
Problem 1 (Possible Solutions)
1. A B K O
$8 + 10 + 10 + 2 = 30$
2. B C I K
$10 + 3 + 7 + 10 = 30$
3. C E I J
$3 + 9 + 7 + 11 = 30$
4. D E F H
$4 + 9 + 1 + 16 = 30$
5. E G L N
$9 + 5 + 12 + 4 = 30$

Page 9
Problem 2
1. E L M S
$9 + 5 + 6 + 10 = 30$
2. F H J M
$1 + 10 + 13 + 6 = 30$
3. G J M Q
$3 + 13 + 6 + 8 = 30$
4. H I P S
$10 + 4 + 6 + 10 = 30$
5. I N R S
$4 + 15 + 1 + 10 = 30$
6. J M R S
$13 + 6 + 1 + 10 = 30$
7. K M O S
$2 + 6 + 12 + 10 = 30$

Odd Triangle Pages 11-12
1. Consecutive odd numbers arranged to form a triangle.
2. Assign a number to each letter.
$a = 1, b = 2, c = 3, d = 4, e = 5, f = 6, g = 7, h = 8, i = 9$
In the odd numbered rows, the middle number is a square of an odd number.
$a = 1$
$c = 3$
$e = 5$
$g = 7$
$i = 9$
Row
3: 7, 9, 11   (9 is the square of 3)
5: 21, 23, 25, 27, 29 (25 is the square of 5)
3. Also in the odd numbered rows, the two end numbers, when averaged, will equal the middle number (square number).
Row
5: 21, 23, 25, 27, 29. $21 + 29 = 50$
Average $= 25 = 5^2$
7: 43, 45, 47, 49, 51, 53, 55.
$43 + 55 = 98$
Average $= 49 = 7^2$
4. In even numbered rows, take the first and last number in the row, add them and divide by 2. Your answer will be the square number for that row.
Row
4: 13, 15, 17, 19
$13 + 19 = 32, 32 \div 2 = 16 = 4^2$
6: 31, 33, 35, 37, 39, 41
$31 + 41 = 72, 72 \div 2 = 36 = 6^2$
5. Search for the digital root. The digital root is a single digit (1, 2, 3, 4, 5, 6, 7, 8, 9).
Example:
$51 = 5 + 1 = 6$
6 is the digital root for 51.
$84 = 8 + 4 = 12, 12 = 1 + 2 = 3$
3 is the digital root for 84.
$277 = 2 + 7 + 7 = 16, 16 = 1 + 6 = 7$
7 is the digital root for 277.

The digital root pattern for the consecutive odd numbers in a triangular formation:

Digital Root

a = 1   1
b = 3 + 5   8
c = 7 + 9 + 11 = 27 = 2 + 7   9
d = 13, 15, 17, 19 = 64 = 6 + 4 = 10 = 1 + 0   1
e = 21, 23, 25, 27, 29 = 125 = 1 + 2 + 5   8
 f = 31, 33, 35, 37, 39, 41 = 216 = 2 + 1 + 6   9
g = 43, 45, 47, 49, 51, 53, 55 = 343 = 3 + 4 + 3 = 10 = 1 + 0   1

You should be able to predict the digital root pattern for the remainder of this series.

High Rise Pages 13-16

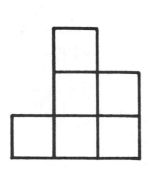

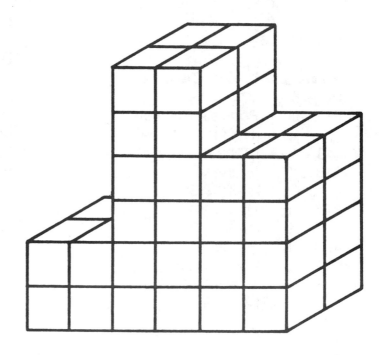

Sample building 6 cubes
Final building 48 cubes
Page 15

Sample Building	Final Building
1. 15 cubes	1. 120 cubes
2. 18 cubes	2. 144 cubes
3. 20 cubes	3. 160 cubes
4. 23 cubes	4. 184 cubes
5. 28 cubes	5. 224 cubes
6. 40 cubes	6. 320 cubes

GA1456

Page 16

Sample Building	Final Building
7. 55 cubes	7. 440 cubes
8. 63 cubes	8. 504 cubes
9. 88 cubes	9. 704 cubes
10. 94 cubes	10. 752 cubes
11. 141 cubes	11. 1128 cubes
12. 426 cubes	12. 3408 cubes

X, 𝕏 Pages 20-22

Page 20

a. = 33
b. = 65
c. = 49
d. = 84
e. = 97
f. = 56
g. = 21
h. = 72

Page 21-22

i. = 15
j. = 47

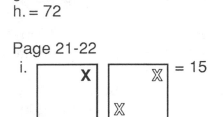

k. = 61

l. = 59

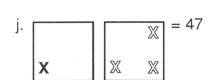

m. = 35

n. = 70
o. = 81

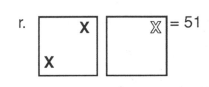

p. = 29
q. = 67

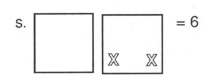

r. = 51
s. = 6

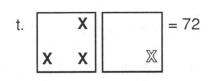

t. = 72
u. = 71
v. = 61

GA1456

Alpha P.V. Pages 33, 34 and 37
Page 33 (Possible Solutions)
1. class = 2120
2. lunch = 1310
3. topic = 1130
4. chalk = 2300
5. paper = 2030
6. grade = 4010

Page 34
1. fame = 3100
2. bake = 3100
3. gale = 3100
4. chef = 3100
5. bide = 3100

Page 37
1. twist = 13.1
2. every = 201.2
3. zesty = 102.2
4. exits = 112.1
5. sweat = 202.1
6. awake = 301.1

Cube It Pages 43-46
Figure A: 24 black squares
30 white squares
Figure B: 36 black squares
18 white squares
Figure C: The point total of white squares is 138.
Figure D: The point total of white squares is 108.
Figure E: The point total of white squares is 180.
The point total of black squares is 90.
Figure F: The point total of white squares is 180.
The point total of black squares is 90.
Figure G: The point value for G is 246.
Figure H: The point value for H is 258.

1492 Page 54
Possibilities
1. create fractions $\frac{1}{9}$, $\frac{2}{4}$
2. create improper fractions $\frac{9}{2}$, $\frac{4}{1}$
3. 1, 4, 9, 2 can be read as Jan. 4, 1992
4. all digits used as factors 4 x 9 x 2 x 1 = 72
5. 1, 4, 9, 2 are related to the months of the year–Jan., Apr., Sept., Feb.
6. 1492 seconds = 24 minutes, 52 seconds
7. 1492 months = 124 years and 4 months
8. 1492 quarters = $373.00
9. 1492 pancakes (each pancake $\frac{1}{8}$" thick) = 186.5"
10. 1492 is a very small number if it represents the number of spectators at a Super Bowl game.
11. 1492 is a very large number if it represents the number of goldfish in the bowl in your house.
12. Use the digits 1, 4, 9, 2 and any operation to write an equation equal to 1. (4 x 2) ÷ (9 - 1) = 1

Make It Happen! Pages 64-67
Possible Solutions

10 $\frac{4 \times 3}{5 + 1} + 8 = 10$

$\frac{8 + 4}{3} + (5 + 1) = 10$

6 $\left[7 + (9\text{-}5)\right] - (3 + 2) = 6$

$\left[5 \times \frac{(7 + 2)}{3}\right] - 9 = 6$

7 $\left[(8\text{-}6) \times 2\right] + (3 \times 1) = 7$

$\left[(8 + 6) - (3 \times 2)\right] - 1 = 7$

9 $\left[(6 + 5) - (3 - 2)\right] - 1 = 9$

$\left[(5 \times 2) - (6 + 1)\right] \times 3 = 9$

GA1456

Common Sense Pages 69-71
1. five-letter words
2. things you can read
3. words with initial letter *P*
4. words beginning and ending with same letter
5. things that go around
6. people who work in a hospital
7. words with a *v* in the middle
8. things that are green
9. things found in water
10. first names of U.S. Presidents
11. factors of 12 or 6
12. multiples of 5
13. things that fly
14. things you can drink
15. words with the letters *s, t, o, p*
16. cities in New Jersey
17. prime numbers
18. factors of 30

Brainteaser XIII Pages 73-74
1. les s (less)
2. me a sure (measure)
3. est tim ate (estimate)
4. ope ration (operation)
5. l in e (line)
6. da ta (data)
7. who le (whole)
8. cur ve (curve)
9. ar c (arc)
10. per,"l met Er (perimeter)
11. sp he re (sphere)
12. min us (minus)
13. ar Ray (array)
14. poly gon (polygon)
15. p Lane (plane)
16. con e (cone)
17. for Ty (forty)
18. ch ord (chord)
19. are a (area)
20. rad l us (radius)
21. p owe R (power)
22. od D (odd)
23. eve n (even)
24. ang "Le (angle)
25. r a Y (ray)
26. 's um (sum)
27. po int (point)
28. gal Lon (gallon)
29. p in t (pint)
30. t wo (two)

Brainteaser XIV Page 76
a. I see you ate my peas.
b. Are you my date?
c. Today I see you won.
d. Why, oh why, are you before us?
e. fifty states
f. waiting for you, too
g. Why are you in my seat?
h. You won. Why are you sad?

Brainteaser XV, Page 77
1. 50 floors
2. 48th floor
3. 35th floor
4. 32nd floor
5. 39th floor
6. 23rd floor

Brainteaser XVI Page 78
On South Madison street there are 30 cars and 23 kids.

Brainteaser XVII Pages 80-81
FOUR = 15
FIVE = 10
SIX = 8
SEVEN = 18
EIGHT = 15
NINE = 11
TEN = 9
ELEVEN = 19
TWELVE = 18
THIRTEEN = 24
FOURTEEN = 28
FIFTEEN = 20
SIXTEEN = 21
SEVENTEEN = 31
EIGHTEEN = 26
NINETEEN = 24
TWENTY = 18
TWENTY-ONE = 29
TWENTY-TWO = 28
TWENTY-THREE = 36
TWENTY-FOUR = 33

GA1456

The Pyramid Page 86

Possible Solutions

A. add = 3
   able = 4
   apple = 5
   admire = 6
   Alabama = 28 (7 x 4)
   Atlantic = 16 (8 x 2)
   advantage = 27 (9 x 3)
   admiration = 20 (10 x 2)
   application = 22 (11 x 2)
   availability = 36 (12 x 3)
   accumulations = 26 (13 x 2)

E. egg = 3
   east = 4
   every = 10 (5 x 2)
   expect = 12 (6 x 2)
   elegent = 21 (7 x 3)
   exercise = 24 (8 x 3)
   emotional = 9
   excitement = 30 (10 x 3)
   environment = 22 (11 x 2)
   entertaining = 24 (12 x 2)
   entertainment = 39 (13 x 3)

I. ink = 3
   inch = 4
   ideal = 5
   insure = 6
   inspect = 7
   identify = 16 (8 x 2)
   imperfect = 9
   invitation = 30 (10 x 3)
   investigate = 22 (11 x 2)
   implications = 36 (12 x 3)
   international = 26 (13 x 2)

O. odd = 3
   only = 4
   occur = 5
   orange = 6
   orderly = 7
   overdone = 16 (8 x 2)
   omissions = 18 (9 x 2)
   obligation = 20 (10 x 2)
   opinionated = 22 (11 x 2)
   overestimate = 12
   orchestration = 36 (13 x 2)

U. use = 3
   unit = 4
   unity = 5
   unions = 6
   unusual = 21 (7 x 3)
   universe = 8
   universal = 9
   understand = 10
   unification = 11
   unaffordable = 12
   underestimate = 13

Beach Party Page 87

Question 1: 91 pieces were on display.
Question 3: a. 210 pieces of fruit
             b. 325 pieces of fruit
             c. 820 pieces of fruit

Alabama to Wyoming Pages 90-91

Problem A:

A	B	C	D	E	F	G	H	I	J	K	L	M
4		3	1		1	1	1	4		2	1	8

N	O	P	Q	R	S	T	U	V	W	X	Y	Z
8	3	1		1	2	2	1	2	4			

Problem B:
Distribution of Letters in Each State Name

Number of Letters	4	5	6	7	8	9	10	11	12	13
Number of States	3	3	5	9	11	6	2	5	3	3

*Alabama, Arizona, Alaska and Ohio

GA1456

Problem C:
1. Number of Times Each Letter Is Used
   to Spell the Fifty State Names
   A-61
   B-2
   C-12
   D-11
   E-28
   F-2
   G-8
   H-15
   I-44
   J-1
   K-10
   L-15
   M-14
   N-43
   O-36
   P-4
   Q-0
   R-22
   S-32
   T-19
   U-8
   V-5
   W-11
   X-2
   Y-6
   Z-1
2. Q
3. 412 letters
4. 8.2 letters

Where's the Number Pages 94-95
Box 5 = 3
Box 6 = 4
Box 7 = 2
Box 8 = 2

5. 3 boxes

6. 4 boxes

7. 2 boxes

8. 2 boxes

The answer is in the lower left-hand corner of each box.

Famous Initials, Pages 97-98
Page 97
   1. Martin Luther King
   2. Franklin Delano Roosevelt
   3. Dwight David Eisenhower
   4. Lyndon Baines Johnson
   5. Harry S. Truman
   6. Richard Milhous Nixon
   7. Edgar Allen Poe
   8. Robert Louis Stevenson
   9. Susan Brownell Anthony
   10. Thomas Alva Edison
   11. Ulysses S. Grant
   12. George Washington Carver
   13. Robert Edward Lee
   14. George Bernard Shaw
   15. Ralph Waldo Emerson
   16. Oliver Wendell Holmes
   17. John Philip Sousa
   18. Henry Wadsworth Longfellow
   19. John Davidson Rockefeller
   20. Julia Ward Howe

GA1456

Page 98
1. George Smith Patton
2. Booker Taliaferro Washington
3. William Jennings Bryan
4. James Fenimore Cooper
5. George Armstrong Custer
6. Mary McLeod Bethune
7. George Michael Cohan
8. William Randolph Hearst
9. Alexander Graham Bell
10. John Quincy Adams